Secrets and Surprises

Third Edition

abeka
Pensacola, FL 32523-9100
an affiliate of PENSACOLA CHRISTIAN COLLEGE®

To Teachers and Parents

Along the way, your student will grow in his love of literature as he reads new stories, poems, and plays. He will practice recognizing and applying phonetic sounds from *Basic Phonics Charts* 8–11. Through special comprehension questions marked with an asterisk, your student will also cultivate thinking/comprehension skills and learn to personally apply valuable lessons.

Secrets and Surprises
Third Edition

Staff Credits
Authors: Laurel Hicks and Marion Hedquist
Managing Editors: Corinne Sawtelle, Connie McBride
Edition Editor: Camilla Kochanowicz
Designer: Michelle Johnson
Illustrators: Brian Jekel, Nadine Voth, and John Ball

Credit: background – Artzone / ©iStockphoto.com

Cataloging Data
Hicks, Laurel.
Secrets and surprises / Laurel Hicks, Marion Hedquist. —3rd ed.
182 p. : col ill. ; 22 cm. (Abeka Book reading program).
1. Readers (Elementary). 2. Reading (Elementary). III. Hedquist, Marion.
IV. Abeka Book, Inc.
Library of Congress: PE1119 .H52 S836 2015
Dewey System: 428.6

Contents

Special sounds from Phonics Charts 8–9 are practiced on pp. 1–59; Phonics Chart 10 is practiced on pp. 64–117; Phonics Chart 11 is practiced on pp. 118–182.

Chart 8

thr in three
ar in stars
ch in church
or in morning
ou in out
ow in owl
ow in bowl
er in verse
ur in nurse
ir in bird
oi in coin
oy in boy
oo in book
oo in tooth
wor in worms
igh in night
all in ball
alk in walk

Chart 9

-ing in pointing
kn in knot
gn in gnat
ang in bang
ing in king
ong in long
ung in strung
ank in bank
ink in wink
onk in honk
unk in trunk
wa in wash
a in adopt
y in baby
le in little
-ed in wanted
-ed in looked
-ed in played

Chart 10

wh in whale
wh in who
tch in patch
ear in ear
ear in bear
ear in earth
old in gold
mb in lamb
ew in flew
ew in few
-y in rainy
-er in bigger
-est in biggest
-ly in slowly
-en in sharpen
-es in peaches
ild in child
ind in kind

Chart 11

o in shovel
a in banana
c in city
au in faucet
aw in saw
ea in leaf
ea in thread
ea in steak
ie in brownie
ey in key
ey in obey
ph in phone
ch in chorus
ought in thought
aught in caught
g in giant
dge in fudge

To Teachers and Parents

Story/Character Themes are presented to encourage appreciation for God's design, recognize His plan for creation, and develop desirable character traits. Discuss themes as stories are read orally, encouraging students to emulate good character traits.

Guide to Story/Character Themes

Words to Practice

zoo
too

farm
start
look

beach
such
better

for
know

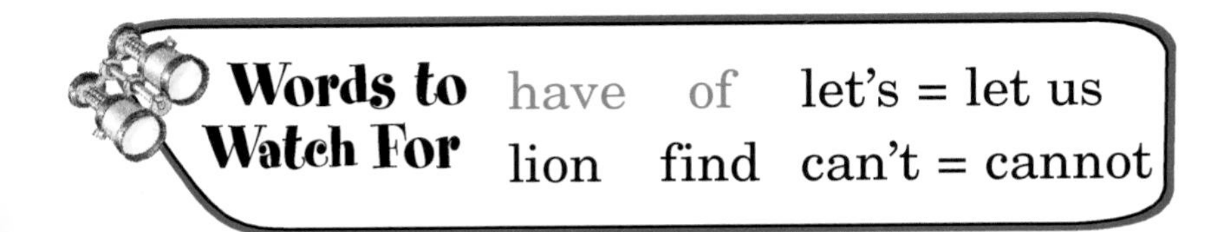

Let's Go!

Marion Hedquist

Let's go to the farm,
Let's go to the zoo,
Let's go to the pond,
And to the beach, too.

Let's look for a lion,
Let's find a fat frog.
Let's hunt for a crab—
Better not take the dog!

Such a time we will have!
Lots of fun, I know.
I can't wait to start—
So please—*let's go!*

swimming	playing
straying	splashing
barking	calling

At the Pond

Marion Hedquist

One fish swimming,
one boy playing,
one frog jumping,
one dog straying.

One girl splashing,

one leaf falling,

one dog barking,

one mom calling:

"Time to go home!"

Words to Watch For

do was lunch
cheese come

Let's Go to the Pond!

Fran and Steve got up one fine day. By ten o'clock the sun felt hot.

"May we go to the pond, Mom?" Steve said. "It will be a good day to wade."

Mom made a lunch for them with cheese, crackers, and fruit. Then she, Fran, and Steve went up the path to the pond. Ruff went with them.

“Sh,” Steve said to Ruff. “You must be still.”

“Do you see the fish splashing, Steve? And look at that big frog,” cried Fran.

The frog sat on a stone. Fran ran up to him. “Jump, frog, jump!” Fran said.

The plump frog did not jump.
"This frog can't jump," said Fran.
"He is much too big."

"Let's get the frog," Steve said.
"Let's take it home for Dad to see."

“Come, frog,” said Fran. “Please let me get you. Please do not jump into the pond.”

Hop. Stop. Hop. Stop. The plump frog did jump!

“Please stop!” said Steve. But the frog did not stop. Plop, plop, plop! It went right into the pond.

“Well, well,” said Fran. “That frog can jump! It can jump fast. Let’s try to get him.”

Fran and Steve got into the water. It was fun to chase the frog. Hop. Stop. Hop, hop, plop, splash!

At last, Fran, Steve, Mom, and Ruff left the pond and the frog. It was time to go home.

"I like to play at the pond," Steve said.

"Yes," said Fran. "Playing tag with a frog is fun!"

Do You Know?

1. What game were they playing with the frog?

*2. Do you think they caught the frog?

*3. What season of the year do you think it is: spring, summer, fall, or winter?

Pond Fun

Look at the pictures. Find the sentence that tells about the picture. Write the number in the box below the sentence.

1

2

3

4

Steve and Fran play tag with the frog. ☐

The plump frog jumps into the pond. ☐

Steve, Fran, Mom, and Ruff go back home. ☐

The plump frog sat on a rock. ☐

Mama four two
one over away

Five Little Ducks

Five little ducks went swimming
one day,
Over the pond and far away.
Mama Duck said, **"Quack, quack,
quack,"**
And four little ducks came
swimming back.

Four little ducks went swimming
one day,
Over the pond and far away.
Mama Duck said, **"Quack, quack,
quack,"**
And three little ducks came
swimming back.

Three little ducks went swimming
one day,
Over the pond and far away.
Mama Duck said, **"Quack, quack,
quack,"**
And two little ducks came
swimming back.

Two little ducks went swimming
one day,
Over the pond and far away.
Mama Duck said, **"Quack, quack,
quack,"**
And one little duck came
swimming back.

One little duck went swimming
one day,
Over the pond and far away.
Mama Duck said, **"Quack, quack,
quack,"**

And no little duck came swimming
back.

Mama Duck went swimming one
day,
Over the pond and far away.
Mama Duck said, **"Quack, quack,
quack,"**
And five little ducks came swimming
back!

Do You Know?

* 1. What happened each time Mama Duck called the little ducks to come?

2. Should the little ducks have stayed with the Mama Duck?

* 3. How do you think the Mama Duck felt when the little ducks did not obey?

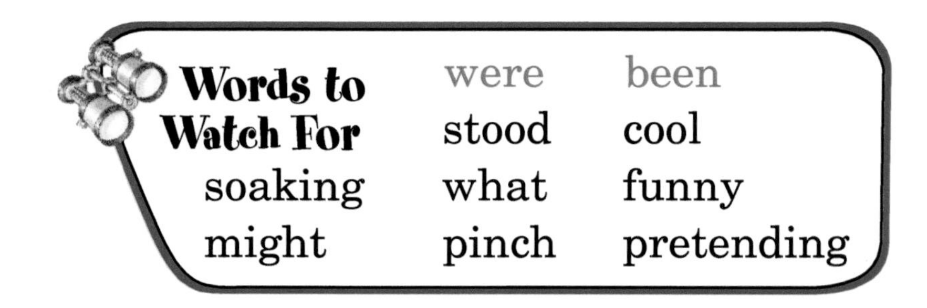

Let's Go to the Beach!

Tom went to the beach one day. He rode in the van with Mom and Dad, and his pal Mike came, too.

“This will be fun!” Tom said. “We can swim all day. I like to go swimming!”

“Please stop the van, Dad!” Tom said. “This looks like a good spot to swim.”

Tom got out of the van and stood on the hot blacktop.

“Ow! That blacktop is too hot for my feet,” he cried. “I can’t stand here. Let’s run to the sand.”

Tom and Mike ran back and forth on the beach.

“The seashore is so much fun, Tom,” Mike said. “I like to feel the hot sun and the cool breeze.” He stood on the sand soaking up the rays of the sun.

“I like to run into the water!” Tom said, and he ran into the waves. Mike ran in after him.

The waves were not high today. The boys had fun running in and out of the water playing tag. Just then Tom felt a little bump on his leg. What was that?

"Look, Mike!" Tom cried. "Do you see what I see?"

Mike said, "Yes! I can see three little fish right here by my legs. Did one of them bump you?"

“Yes,” Tom said, “but it did not bite.” He began to giggle. “It felt funny.”

The boys ran out of the water onto the beach.

“Look, Mike,” Tom cried. “Look at that crab. See the funny way he runs! I’m glad I don’t run like that. He goes sideways.” Tom got up close for a good look.

“Get back a little, Tom,” Mike said. “He might pinch you.”

The boys ran back down the beach sideways, pretending to be crabs.

At last it is time to go home.

"I hate to leave the beach," Tom said. "It has been a lot of fun."

"I am glad I came with you," said Mike. "Thank you for asking me. Maybe next week you can go to the zoo with me!"

Proverbs 18:24

"A man that hath friends must shew himself friendly."

Do You Know?

* 1. Use the picture on page 18 to tell how Tom and Mike knew that it was time to go home.

* 2. How do you know that Tom and Mike are good friends?

3. Where did Mike think the boys might be able to go next week?

Beach Fun

Look at the pictures. In the boxes beside the pictures, put a 1, 2, or 3 to show what happened first, second, and third in the story.

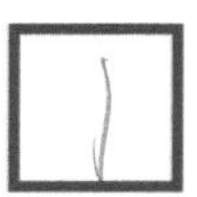

Words to Watch For every when

Jesus Sees Me

Jesus sees me
When I sleep.
Jesus sees me
When I play.
Jesus sees me
All the time,
Every night and
Every day!

Psalm 56:3

"What time I am afraid, I will trust in Thee."

Words to Watch For

down	wooden
they	sandy
empty	could

At the Sea

Robert Louis Stevenson

When I was down beside the sea,
A wooden spade they gave to me
  To dig the sandy shore.
My holes were empty like a cup;
In every hole the sea came up
  Till it could come no more.

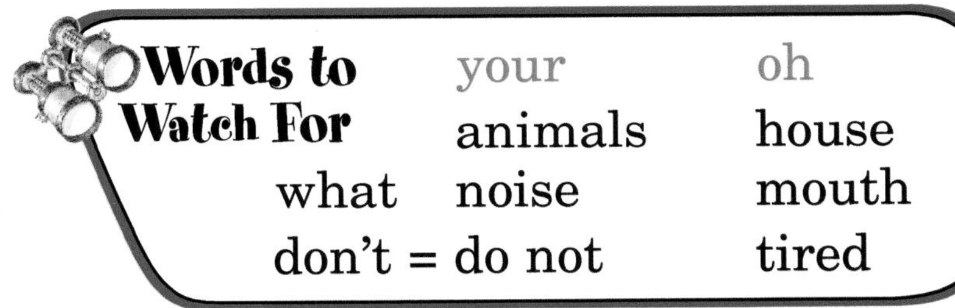
Words to Watch For

what
don't = do not
your
animals
noise
oh
house
mouth
tired

Let's Go to the Zoo!

Mike's dad took Tom and Mike to the zoo. They all rode in a pickup truck.

See the boys jump out! They will see so much today.

"Let's run to the gate," Mike said. "I can't wait to see all the animals!"

Mike's dad gave cash to the boys, and the boys paid the man at the gate.

"Let's walk on this path first," Mike's dad said. "I think I can see an elephant!"

"Yes, I see him too," Mike spoke up. "Look at his trunk. He is as big as a house!"

"Well, maybe not a house, but he is big," Mike's dad said with a grin.

The boys came to a pond next.

"I can see a big, gray animal," Mike cried out. "I do not know what it is. Do you know what kind of animal that is, Tom?"

Tom got up close to the rail. He got a good look at the big animal. "No, Mike, I have not seen an animal like this before. But I am glad my nose is not that big!"

Just then the big gray animal stood up. He made a loud noise.

"What is this animal?" Mike said to his dad. "Do you know?"

"Yes, I do. It is a hippopotamus," Dad said.

Mike tried to say *hippopotamus.* "I can't say that!" Mike said.

"Well, we can make a short name for him. You can call him a hippo," his dad said.

"Look at his mouth," Tom cried. "See the big teeth! What a big toothbrush he must use!"

The boys ran down the path. Tom saw a big pen.

The pen had a tree in it and a brown animal.

"Do you see what I see?" Tom said to Mike.

"Yes, it is a monkey!" Mike said. "See him run and jump on the tree. I will stand close to the pen. I hope he will see me. I'm going to try to get him to wave at me."

“Look out, Mike!” Tom cried. “He is hopping down the branch. I am glad he cannot reach you.”

“Look, Tom,” Mike said. “He sees his ball by the tree trunk. It would be fun to play ball with a monkey.”

“I see a tall animal,” Mike’s dad said. “See the long neck God gave him.”

“Oh, my,” cried Mike. “I hope he will not get a sore throat! It will hurt a lot.”

“See what the giraffe can do with his long neck,” said Tom. “He can eat the leaves right off the top of the trees.”

“We must go soon,” said Mike’s dad, “but let’s go down this path first. There may be more animals we can look at.”

“See the big cat sleep in the sun on that rock,” Tom cried. “It is a tiger!”

“Yes,” Mike said, “I like his black stripes. He looks like my cat at home. But I don’t think I will try to play with this cat. He is not tame.”

The boys got into the truck. They were tired, but it had been a good day. They had a lot to talk about.

"I am glad you took me to the zoo," Tom said. "I am glad I got to see all the animals God made."

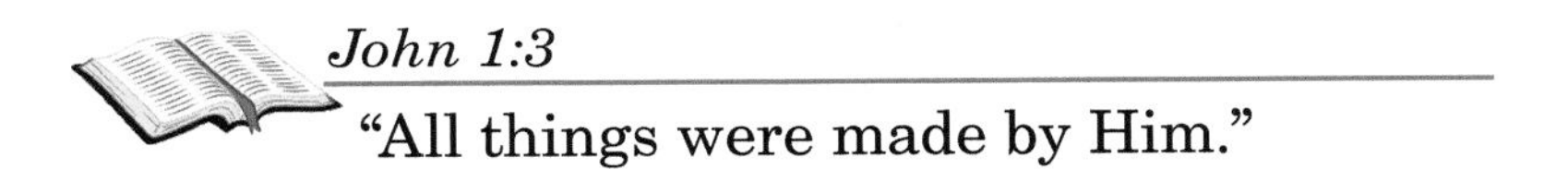

John 1:3

"All things were made by Him."

Do You Know?

* 1. Why do you think God may have given the tiger black stripes?

* 2. Why do you think that the boys were tired at the end of the day?

3. Did God make all of the animals in the world?

4. What is your favorite animal to see at the zoo?

Zoo Fun

Color just the five animals that Mike and Tom saw at the zoo. Then number those five animals 1, 2, 3, 4, 5 in the order that the boys saw them at the zoo.

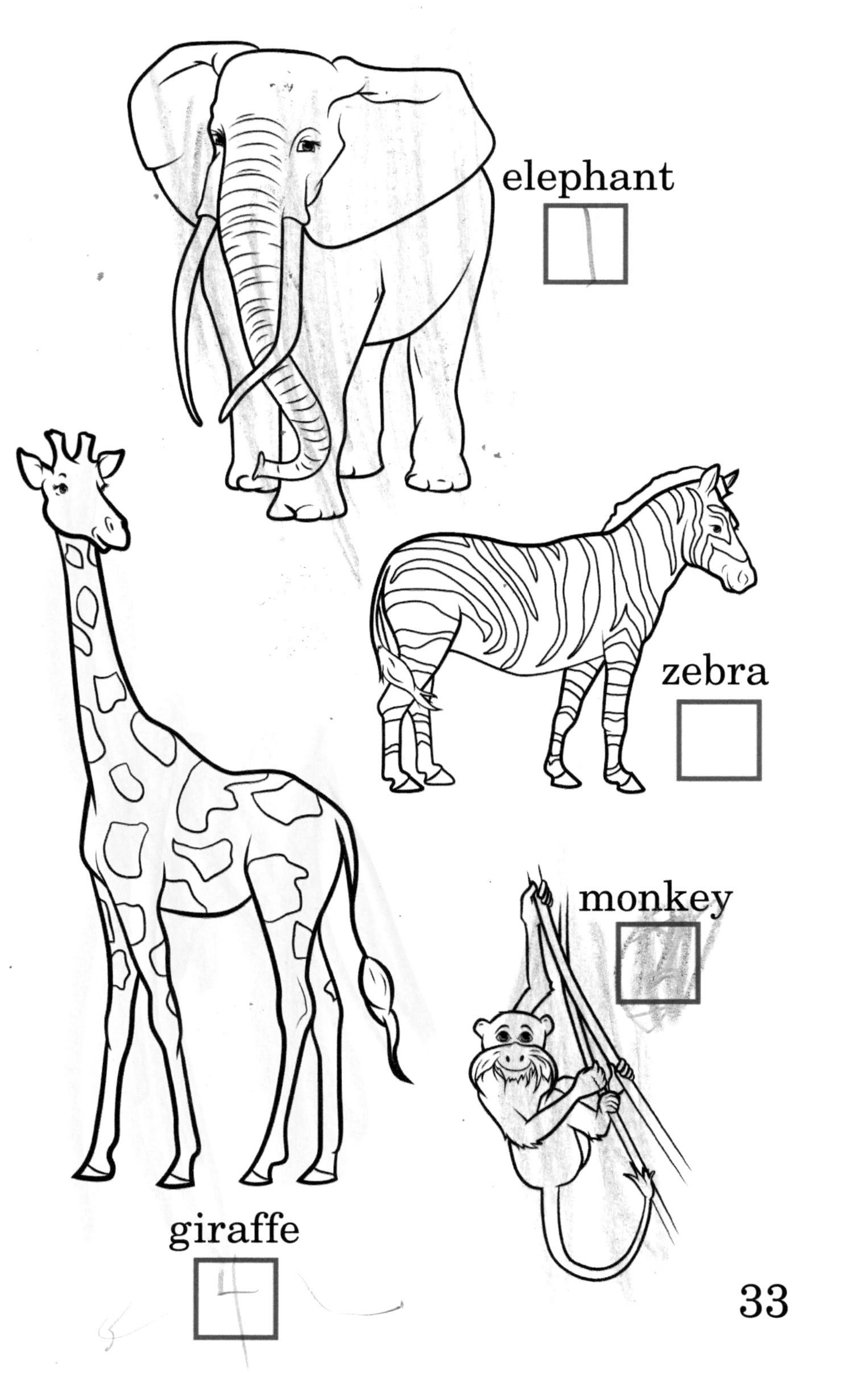
elephant
zebra
monkey
giraffe

small whiskers

Dad

Marion Hedquist

Mike's dad is big,
And Bill's dad is small.
Chad's dad has whiskers
And is six feet tall!

Mike's dad takes us to the zoo.
Bill's dad likes to play ball.
But my dad belongs to *me,*
And he's the *best* dad of all!

Words to Practice

Read the special sounds and words.

ow in owl, ow in bowl

cow show howl how now

ar in stars

Barb card hard barnyard

ou in out

counts our proud

wor in worms

word work

Read these words quickly.

water	horse	farmer
spring	grow	ground
gather	fall	thank

love would
we're = we are

Going to the Farm

Marion Hedquist

May I ride the horse?
May I milk the cow?
(If I miss the can,
Will you show me how?)

May I take water
And grain to the hen?
(I'll run by the pig—
It stinks in his pen!)

I love the farm!
I wish Dad would say,
"We're not going home,
We're here to stay!"

Words to Watch For

Taylor	news
Grandma	Grandpa
when	others

Let's Go to the Farm!

Taylor was in the backyard.

"Taylor," said Mom. "Come inside. I have news for you!" Taylor ran into the house. "I got a text from Grandma. She wants us to come to the farm," said Mom.

"Oh, Mom," Taylor said. "May we go to the farm? I want to visit Grandpa and Grandma. May we go next week? Please?"

Mom had a big smile. "We will ask Dad," she said. "I think he will say we can go."

At last the big day came.

Mom, Dad, Taylor, and Max drove all day long. Taylor sang songs until Max began to howl. He was trying to sing, too!

"Let's play a word game," Dad said. "Look for something that begins with the letter *a,* then *b,* then *c,* all the way to *z.*"

It was fun playing games in the car.

At last they got to the farm, and Taylor got out of the car. She was glad to be at the farm at last.

"Look at Max," Taylor said. "He is glad to be here, too. See him jump out of the back seat. Look at him run and chase his tail."

"Let's go see the animals, Max. Look at the pig. You must not chase him, or you might end up in the mud, too. He eats a lot of pig food, and he grunts as he eats it."

"Oink, oink."

"I am glad I do not make noise when I eat!"

“Look at the cow, Max. She is black and white. You must not chase her.”

“We can get good milk from her. I like to pat her. She is so soft!”

"Look at the hen, Max. You must not chase her. See her pecking at the grain Grandpa left in the barnyard for her. She likes to eat it. She must be a good mother. She keeps her baby chicks with her all the time. Soon she will lay an egg. Maybe Grandma will fix ham and eggs. Yum!"

“Look at all the sheep in the pen, Max. I can count nine of them. You must not chase them. I like to feel the wool on the sheep’s back. Did you hear the sheep bleat? That is how he talks to his wife!”

"See the pond, Max. Is that a duck on the water? Maybe she will swim by us, but you must not chase her."

"Oh, look! She has baby ducks with her. How cute!"

"I am tired, Max. It has been a long day, our first day at the farm. I am glad we will be here a week."

"We have a lot more to see yet. Grandma said that one of the barn cats had kittens. Dad said that we can do jobs, too. It will be fun to do jobs at the farm."

"In the morning I will feed the pigs and the chickens. Maybe I can take grain to the cows, too. I will work hard so Dad can be proud of me.

Then I will go for a short ride on the horse."

"Wait! I hear a dog barking. It must be Max. No, no, Max!"

"You must not chase the hen. She will not like it, and you might hurt her or one of her baby chicks. I must get your leash. If we do bad things, we will hurt others."

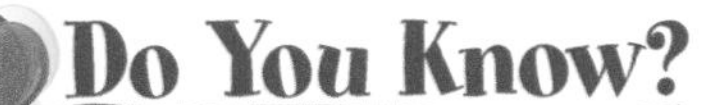

Do You Know?

1. What does the cow give that is good for us?

2. Name some jobs that Taylor wanted to do on the farm.

*3. Do you think these jobs would be easy? Why?

Words to Watch For
give course
tractor why from

Farming

Janice Sherwin

The farmer plants the seeds in spring
  That grow up green and tall.
His tractor helps him work the ground
  And gather crops in fall.

Animals help the farmer, too—
  A dog, a cat, a horse.
Sheep grow wool, hens lay eggs,
  And cows give milk, of course.

God helps the farmer do his work,
  For God makes all things grow.
That's why we thank God for our food.
  It comes from Him, we know.

Farm Helpers

What do these animals give us? Draw lines to match. Color the pictures.

Words to Watch For

where white
blows slow

Clouds

Christina Rossetti

White sheep, white sheep,
On a blue hill,
When the wind stops
You all stand still.
When the wind blows
You walk away slow.
White sheep, white sheep,
Where do you go?

Words to Practice

-ing in pointing

camping	fishing	peeking
cooking	setting	looking
sleeping	seeing	sitting

Read these words quickly.

smooth	bring	worm
hook	strung	jerk
moon	strong	sturdy
zipper	swung	soon

Camping

Marion Hedquist

Setting up the tent,
Camping by the lake,
Fishing with a pole,
Looking for a snake!

Cooking on a fire,
Seeing Ruff's tail wag,
Peeking at the moon
From my sleeping bag.

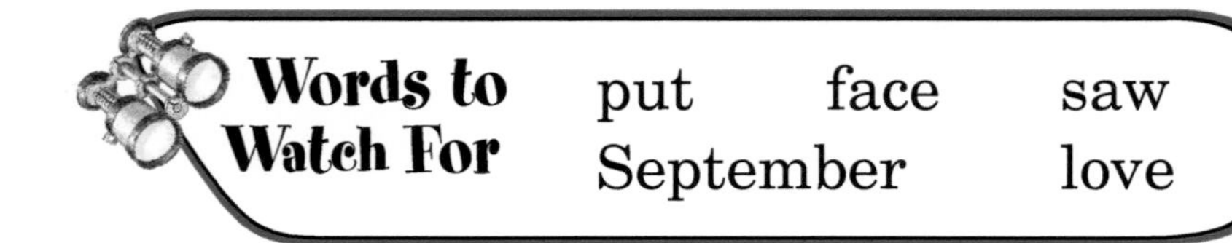

Let's Go Camping!

Dad put the tent in the back of the truck and shut the tailgate. Then Todd got into the cab. He had his sleeping bag in his hand.

"This will be lots of fun, Dad! I am so glad we get to go camping."

Dad smiled, "I am glad, too!"

"Do we get to eat hot dogs, Dad? I like hot dogs."

"No," Dad said. "We will not eat hot dogs this time." Dad had a big grin on his face. "We will eat a meal that we get with a pole," he said.

"A pole!" Todd cried.

Todd saw his dad's grin. "Is this a joke?"

"No, it is not a joke," his dad said.

Just then Todd saw the fishing poles in the back of the truck. He let out a squeal.

"We get to go fishing!" he cried. "Yes, this will be *lots* of fun! The last time we went fishing was in June, and this is September. I love to go fishing!"

Todd and his dad drove for a long time.

At last Todd saw the lake.

Dad said, "This is the spot. We will camp by that big tree." He drove the truck close to the tree, and they got out.

Dad said, "Todd, get the fishing poles. I will get the tent."

Todd got the poles. "May I help you with the tent, Dad?"

Todd's dad let him help. First Todd got to pick the spot where the ground was flat and smooth. Then Dad let him bring the tent spikes and help lay out the tent.

Dad drove the spikes into the ground as Todd got the sleeping bags. Soon the tent was up.

"That tent is big!" Todd said. "Will it stay up?"

"Oh, yes," Dad said. "This tent is strong and sturdy. Zip up the zipper in the door, and let's go fishing!"

Todd ran to get the fishing poles and bait, and off they went to the lake. Soon Todd was sitting on a tree stump with his pole.

He put a worm on his hook and put the line into the water.

Todd's dad sat on a stump by him. He said, "We must be still now, Todd."

It felt good to sit and soak up the sun.

Just then Todd felt a jerk on his line and saw a fish splash.

His dad said, "You got a bass, Todd!"

Todd cried, "It's a big one, Dad! I hope I can keep it on my line." Todd's dad came to help him.

Just then, Todd swung the line back, and the fish hit the bank by Todd.

"You got it, Todd!" his dad said.

Todd had a big grin. "May I clean it now, Dad? I can't wait to eat it!"

Todd got to help clean the fish, and then it was time to pick up sticks for the fire. Dad fried Todd's fish in a big pan over the fire, and they ate it with beans. That fish did taste good!

That night Todd lay in his sleeping bag. His dad was near him. Todd felt good inside. It was fun to camp with his dad.

It was fun to fish in the lake and then eat the fish. It was fun to sleep in a tent.

Todd saw the moon peeking in the flap of the tent. Todd said, "Dad, God is good to us!"

Do You Know?

1. What kind of fish did Todd catch?

*2. How had God been good to Todd?

*3. How has God been good to you?

Which One?

Mark the ○ by the sentence in each box that tells what happened in the story.

Dad and Todd drove to the lake in a car.	○
Dad and Todd drove to the lake in a truck.	○

Todd got a big bass.	○
Dad got a big bass.	○

Todd ate hot dogs by the fire.	○
Todd ate fish by the fire.	○

Words to Watch For

Daddy — interstate

doesn't = does not

Interstate

Laurel Hicks

When Daddy doesn't
  want to be late,
He drives to work
  on the interstate.

laughed hey
getting children

Hey Diddle Diddle

Hey diddle diddle,
The cat and the fiddle,
The cow jumped over the moon.
The little dog laughed
To see such sport,
And the dish ran
away with the spoon.

I See the Moon

I see the moon,
And the moon sees me;
God bless the moon,
And God bless me.

Man in the Moon

The Man in the Moon looked
  out of the moon,
And this is what he said:
"Now that I'm getting up,
  it's time
All children went to bed."

Words to Practice

Suffixes *come at the end of a root word to make a new word. Practice these suffix words.*

-ed in looked ("t")

thank	help	ask	check
thanked	helped	asked	checked
watch	miss	peck	peek
watched	missed	pecked	peeked

-ed in played ("d")

call	starve	agree	hug
called	starved	agreed	hugged
moan	pray	turn	curl
moaned	prayed	turned	curled

-ed in wanted ("ĕd")

count	point	start	wait
counted	pointed	started	waited

-en

eat	fall
eaten	fallen

-y -ly

greed	near
greedy	nearly

Words to Watch For

Grandma's glasses
folds Grandpa's

Grandma's Glasses

Here are Grandma's glasses;
Here is Grandma's hat;
This is the way she folds her hands
And lays them in her lap.

Here are Grandpa's glasses;
Here is Grandpa's hat;
This is the way he folds his arms,
Just like that.

Words to Practice

wiggle	giggle	twins	grins
chins	word	bird	third

Meet Beth and Brad

Marion Hedquist

Beth and Brad think it's
fun to be twins,
With two times the giggles
and two times the grins.
We'll learn things with them
about candy and birds—
Looking for the cat and
trusting God's Words.

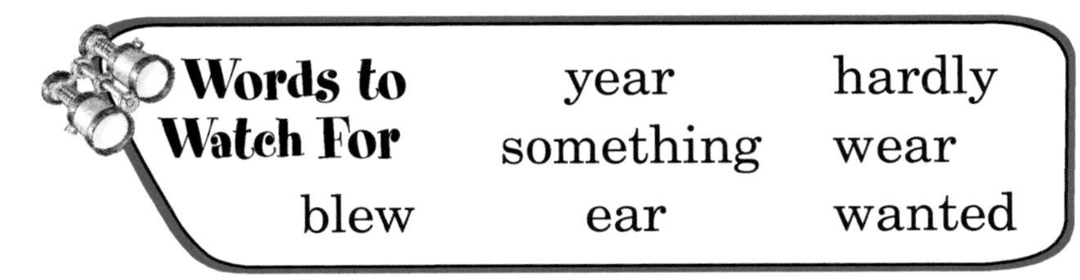

Birthday Surprise

Brad and Beth are twins. Beth is a girl, and Brad is a boy. They are five right now, but soon they will be six.

The twins went to kindergarten last year, and now they can read well. They like to read books at home to Mom and Dad. Mom and Dad are proud of them.

Beth and Brad have the same birthday. Mom is going to bake them a cake in the shape of the number six. The twins can hardly wait!

At last the big day came. Just before lunch time, the doorbell rang. Ding! Dong! Brad ran to the door. The mailman had a box for the twins. It had Grandma's name in the corner.

What was in the box? Was it something to wear? Was it books or a game? Mom said they must wait, but, oh, it was so hard to wait!

At last it was time to cut the cake. The twins ran to the table and waited for Mom.

"I'm glad God gave us the same birthday," Beth said. "It's fun to be twins!"

They made a wish and blew hard. They blew out all the candles!

Just before Mom cut the cake, they prayed. They thanked God for the cake and for making them twins. At last they got to eat birthday cake!

Ding! Dong! The doorbell rang, and Beth ran to the door this time. What a surprise!

"Grandma!" Beth cried with a grin from ear to ear. "How did you get here?"

Grandma hugged Brad and Beth.

"I wanted to surprise you," she said. "I came on the plane. I came to see if you like the gift I sent you for your birthday."

Beth took the bow off the box, and Brad took off the paper and the lid.

"Oh, Grandma! We do like the gift," the twins cried. The box had a lot of books in it.

"We love to read," Beth said. "We will read all of these books for you."

"I hope you will," Grandma said with a smile.

"I like the gift," Brad spoke up, "but the best thing we got for our birthday is *you*." And Brad stuck the bow on Grandma!

Do You Know?

*1. Why did Beth and Brad have only one birthday cake?

*2. Do you think Beth and Brad were glad that they were twins? How do you know?

*3. Do you think that Grandma lives nearby? Why?

Draw a Twin

Draw a twin for a boy or girl. Follow the steps to make your twin look just like the one pictured.

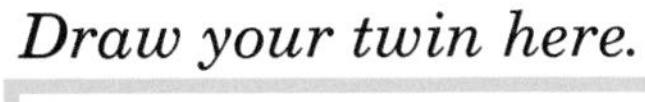

Birthday Fun

Look at the pictures. Number them 1–4 in the order that things happened in the story. Put the numbers in the boxes.

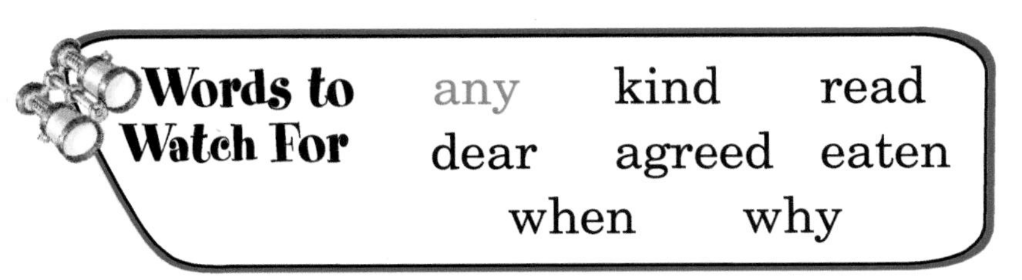

Getting Too Much

Ding! Dong! Ding! Dong!

"The doorbell is ringing," Brad called.

"I will get it," Beth said, and she ran to the door. The mailman stood on the step. He had a box for Brad and Beth.

The box had Grandma's name on it.

"This box can't be for our birthday," Beth said. "We just had our birthday."

"How kind of Grandma to send us a gift! What is it for?"

"May we open the box, Mom?" Brad asked.

"Let me read the card first," Mom said.

She took the card off the side of the box. Then she read out loud,

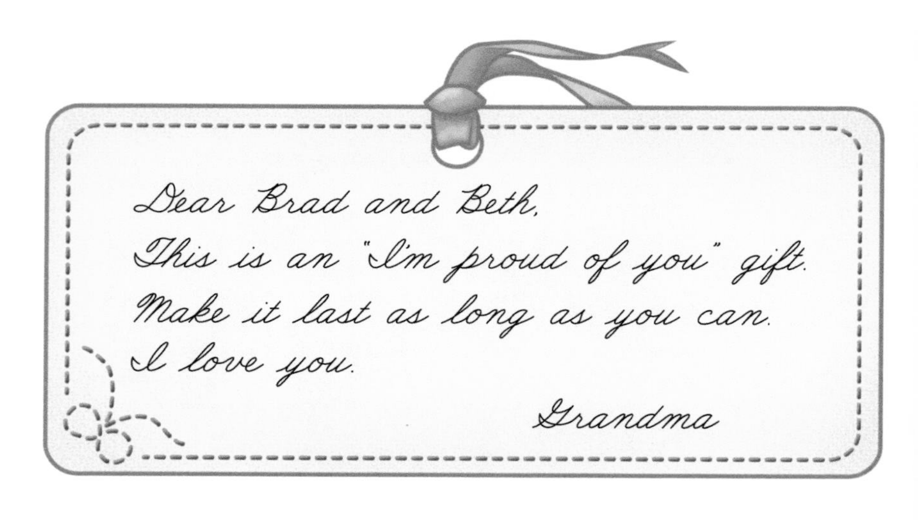
Dear Brad and Beth,
This is an "I'm proud of you" gift.
Make it last as long as you can.
I love you.
Grandma

"Yes, you may open the box," Mom said. Brad and Beth tore the box open.

"Wow! Look at this," Brad cried.

The box had candy in it—lots of candy. The twins counted the candy and made two piles.

Beth said, "I am going to make my candy last for two weeks."

"I am, too," Brad agreed.

"That is wise," Mom said.

Brad took his candy to his room. He looked and looked at it. It looked so good! He chose one candy bar and ate it. Then he went to play ball.

When he came back to his room, he looked at the candy. It looked so good, and he felt starved! Brad took more candy, and then he took more. He did not stop until he had eaten all the candy!

When it was time to eat supper, Brad felt sick. He did not want to eat a thing. He said, "May I go to my room and lie down? I do not feel well."

Mom looked at Brad. Then she looked at Dad and smiled. "Yes, you may go to your room," she said.

"Brad, this is shrimp!" Beth said. "It is the meal we like best!"

"Not tonight," Brad moaned. "I am sick." He got up and went to bed.

The next day, Brad felt fine. He and Beth got out bikes to go for a ride.

"Wait!" Beth said. "Let's take a candy bar with us. It will taste good when we get hot and tired."

"I can't," Brad had to tell her. "I ate all my candy."

"Brad, is that why you were sick last night? Is that why you did not want to eat shrimp?"

"Yes," Brad said, "and now you will get to eat candy for two more weeks. I will not get to eat any. I wish I had made a better choice and not eaten all of my candy."

Do You Know?

1. What was the twins' favorite meal?

2. When did Beth want to eat a candy bar?

Sentence Match

Which picture matches the sentence? Mark the ○ under the correct picture.

1. The mailman came up the walk.

○ ● ○

2. Brad and Beth are riding bikes.

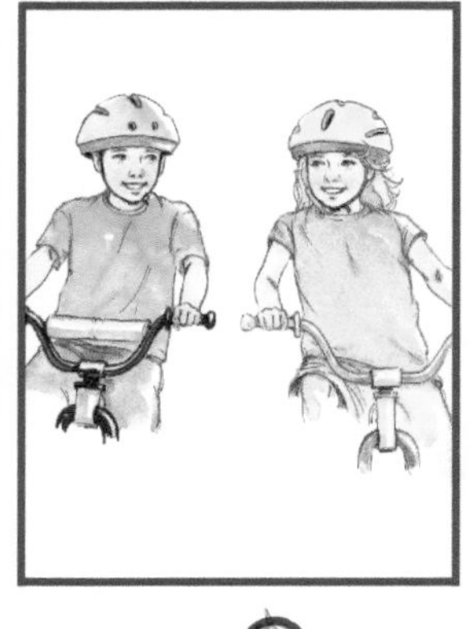

○ ○ ●

Words to Watch For

few flew new

A Few Riddles with ew

Draw lines to match the riddle with the picture.

This baby said, "Mew."

This baby will chew!

This baby flew down our street.

This baby grew little feet.

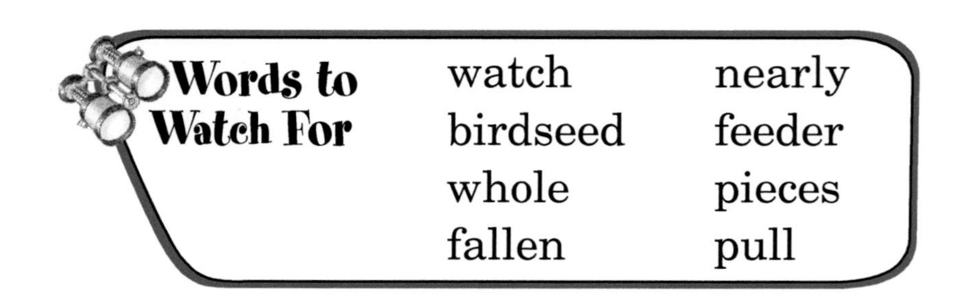

Brad's Secret

"Beth, it is time to go," Brad called. Beth looked at her watch. It was nearly three o'clock.

"Here I come," Beth called.

She got her purse and ran down the steps. It was time to walk to the store with Grandma.

Grandma and Brad were waiting for Beth.

"I love to stay with you, Grandma!" Beth said. "It's fun to walk to the store on your street."

Grandma smiled. "Spring days are good days for walks," she said. "I like to see the flowers and the bright green leaves on the trees."

Soon they were at the door of the little store.

"What will you get, Beth?" Brad asked.

"I am going to get birdseed," Beth said.

"If you get birdseed," Brad said, "I will get yarn."

"Yarn?" Beth asked. "Why do you want to get yarn? What will you do with it?"

Brad smiled a secret smile. "You will see," he said.

Beth got three bags of birdseed, and Brad got red, blue, and green yarn. When they got home, they ran to the bird feeder in the backyard.

"I'm so glad Grandpa made this for us!" Brad said. "It will be fun to feed the birds."

"Yes," Beth said, "we can look for all kinds of birds. I like blue jays best."

Then she looked at Brad. "But what will you do with the yarn?" she asked.

"You will see," Brad said with a smile.

That day the twins watched for birds. The first bird to come to the feeder was a robin. They liked his red tummy. It was fun to see him peck the seed. They saw a finch and a blue jay, too. It did not take long for them to see that the blue jay was a bully. He wanted the whole bird feeder for himself!

That night Brad took the yarn to his room. He cut the yarn into short pieces. He had short pieces of red, blue, and green. Then he got out a brown bag of pine cones.

He had picked up the pine cones from Grandma's yard. They had fallen from a pine tree. Now he had a way to use them. He took a few short pieces of yarn and stuck them into two pine cones.

The ends of the pieces of yarn hung out. Brad looked at his pine cones and smiled. They looked odd!

The next day Brad took the two pine cones to the backyard.

Just then Beth ran down the back steps. She looked at the pine cones. “What will you do with those things?” she asked.

“I will set these in the backyard,” Brad said. “I think the birds will like them.”

“What will the birds do with pine cones and yarn?” Beth asked. “Will they eat them?”

Brad just smiled. "You will see," he said.

Each day the twins checked the pine cones. Each day they counted the pieces of yarn.

At first just a few pieces of yarn were missing—then more and more.

Then one day they saw a robin fly down to a pine cone. With its beak it pecked at a piece of yarn. They saw the bird pull it out and fly away.

"Quick!" Brad said. "Let's see if it has a nest." They ran after the bird. The bird flew up into a little tree.

"I can see the nest!" Brad cried. "Can you see it, Beth?"

Beth looked up into the tree. She saw bits of red, green, and blue.

"Yes," she said. "Now I see what the birds do with the yarn. They use it to help make a good nest. Then the bird will lay eggs in her nest."

"Brad," Beth asked, "how do you think a bird knows the right way to make a nest? The nest has to be strong so that the rain will not wash it away."

"I think I know," Brad said. "I think God tells the bird how to do it. She can't read a book, so God just makes her so that she knows!"

"This has been fun, Brad. I will tell Mom that today I helped make a new red, green, and blue home right in Grandma's backyard!"

Do You Know?

1. What started happening to the pieces of yarn in the pine cones?

2. Who was taking the pieces of yarn?

*3. Which does a bird do first, lay her eggs or build her nest? Why?

What Happened First?

Number these pictures in the order that they took place in the story.

Words to Watch For once window

Once I Saw a Little Bird

Once I saw a little bird
Come hop, hop, hop,
And I cried, "Little Bird,
Will you stop, stop, stop?"

I was going to the window
To say, "How do you do?"
But he shook his little tail
And away he flew.

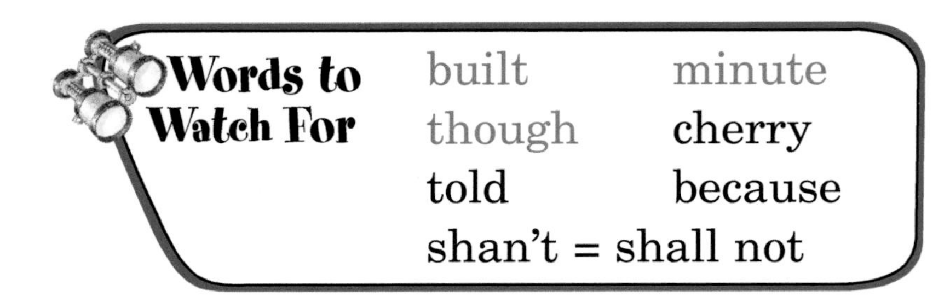
Words to Watch For
built
minute
though
cherry
told
because
shan't = shall not

The Secret

Author Unknown

We have a secret, just we three,
The robin and I,
  and the sweet cherry tree,—
The bird told the tree,
  and the tree told me,
And nobody knows it
  but just we three.

But of course, the robin knows best,
Because he built the—
  I shan't tell the rest;
And laid the four little—
  something in it—
I'm afraid I shall tell it
  every minute.

But if the tree and the
  robin don't peep,
I'll try my best the secret to keep;
Though I know when
  the little birds fly about,
Then the whole secret will be out.

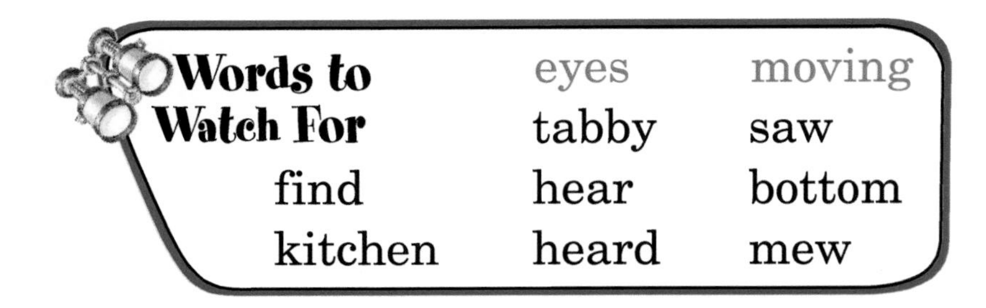
Words to Watch For

	eyes	moving
	tabby	saw
find	hear	bottom
kitchen	heard	mew

Puff's Surprise

Beth was looking for her cat. "Puff, Puff!" she called.

Puff was Beth's tabby cat. Puff liked to play with Beth. She liked to chase yarn and string. She liked to play with big gift bags.

She liked to curl up by Beth and sleep. But Beth had not seen Puff all day. Beth found Brad in his room.

"Brad, have you seen Puff?" she asked. "I have not seen her all day."

"No, I haven't seen her," Brad said. "Have you looked outside?"

"I will look in the backyard," Beth said, and she ran out the door.

"Puff, Puff!" Beth called in the backyard. Then she saw something moving.

It was in a hole under the back step. Beth ran to the hole and peeked in. Puff peeked out at her.

The next day Beth did her chores. Then she and Brad went for a bike ride.

When they got back, Beth missed Puff. She called, "Puff, Puff!"

"I saw her in the den this morning," Brad said.

"The den," Beth said. "I did not go to the den this morning. Let's see if we can find her."

The twins ran into the den.

"Puff! Are you here?" Beth called. They did not hear a sound. Beth turned on the light, and they looked all around the room.

"Here she is!" Beth called. Brad bent down and saw Puff.

She was sleeping on the bottom shelf of a bookcase.

"Puff, why are you here?" Beth asked. She picked Puff up and took her to her room.

The next day Beth got the cat food and went to Puff's dish to feed her.

"Puff," she called, but Puff did not run to the dish today.

Beth found her mom in the kitchen.

"Mom, Puff will not play with me," Beth said. "She hides from me in little corners. Is she mad at me?"

"No, I do not think so," Mom said. "I think she is looking for the right spot. She is planning a surprise for you." Beth told Brad about the surprise.

“A surprise?” Brad asked. “What kind of surprise?”

“I do not know,” Beth said, “but I hope it will be a good one. I do not want her to run away.”

The twins looked and called for Puff.

Just then Dad called from the basement. “Are you looking for Puff?” he asked. “She is down here.”

The twins ran down the steps. Dad pointed to a box in a dark corner. Beth saw Puff's green eyes shining.

"Puff!" she cried. "Why are you here?" She bent down to pick Puff up.

Just then Beth heard a noise. Something said, "Mew."

"Oh, Brad!" Beth cried. "I know what Puff's surprise is! Look in the box!" In the box Brad saw six baby kittens.

"Oh, wow!" Brad said. "I like your surprise, Puff!"

And Puff looked up as if to say, "Thank you! I'm glad you like it!"

Do You Know?

1. What was the noise that Beth heard?

2. Did the twins like Puff's surprise?

3. How many kittens did Puff have?

Puff's Hiding Places

Where did Puff hide? Mark the ○ under the pictures that show where Puff hid.

More -ed Words

Circle the correct word to complete each sentence.

Dad had to _____ the car.

park parked

The vase broke when Pam _____ it.

drop dropped

I hope it will not _____ to rain.

start started

We love to _____ to God.

pray prayed

The cat _____ into Beth's lap.

jump jumped

Words to Practice

Read these suffix words.

-ed in looked		-ed in played	
dress	rush	frown	grin
dressed	rushed	frowned	grinned
brush	wink	scrub	open
brushed	winked	scrubbed	opened
park	wish	twirl	spray
parked	wished	twirled	sprayed

Review these sight words.

both	guess	Mrs.	Mr.
shoe	their	who	very

Review these words quickly.

knew	front	behind
school	would	always
phone	face	warm

Beth's Secret

Beth and Brad got in the car after church. They were both talking at once.

Beth said, "Mom, guess what we found out today!"

Brad did not wait for Mom to guess. He told her, "Mrs. Smith is going away. We will have a new teacher next week."

Mrs. Smith was Beth and Brad's Sunday school teacher. The twins were sad all the way home.

They loved Mrs. Smith. They were going to miss her. Brad would miss Mr. Smith, too. He had helped with the class lots of times.

Dad told the twins, "Let's trust God. After all, His way is always best. Let's pray that He will send the right teacher to your class."

That week, Beth and Brad both prayed.

Saturday night, Beth heard Mom talk on the phone. She ran to find Brad.

"I know a secret!" she said with a big smile.

"Oh, Beth, tell me, tell me!" Brad cried.

"You will find out in the morning," Beth said. "And you will like the secret." She would not tell him any more.

The next morning, Brad heard Beth in her room. She was getting dressed for Sunday school.

Brad heard Beth hum to herself. He knew she was happy. He dropped a shoe on his toe. Ouch!

That hurt! He wished he knew the secret, too. Then he heard Beth start to sing. Brad had to smile.

He got out his new shirt. Maybe Mom would let him wear it. He brushed his teeth and scrubbed his face till it shone.

Soon Beth and Brad were all dressed. They got their Bibles and got into the car.

Soon Mom and Dad came too, and they were on their way to church. Beth talked all the way.

The twins jumped out as soon as Dad parked the car. They rushed down the hall to their Sunday school class. Brad looked all around. No teacher was in sight! He looked at Beth.

She just grinned at him. Brad sat down by James. James looked around, too.

"Do you know who our new teacher is, Brad?"

"No," Brad started to say. Just then the door opened. Brad's mom walked up to the front of the class.

She looked at Beth and Brad and winked. Brad heard Beth giggle. All of a sudden he felt warm inside—and very happy. A big smile came across his face.

"Yes, James, I do know who our teacher is," Brad said.

"And you will like her a lot." Brad grinned at his mom. "She's my mom!" he said. God did hear him pray. He sent the best teacher!

Do You Know?

*1. How did God answer Brad's prayer?

2. Was Brad happy with the way God answered his prayer?

3. Does God always answer our prayers in the best possible way?

The Sunday School Secret

Which picture matches the sentence? Mark the ○ under the correct picture.

1. Brad got ready for Sunday school.

○ ○ ○

2. Beth heard Mom talking on the phone.

○ ○ ○

3. Brad and Beth rode home in the car.

4. Brad dropped a shoe on his toe.

tomorrow hair
because

Wash My Hair

Laurel Hicks

Wash my hair,
Wash my hair,
Scrub, scrub, scrub.

Dry my hair,
Dry my hair,
Rub, rub, rub.

Brush my hair,
Brush my hair;
I'll sit still in my seat.

Because tomorrow is Sunday
school,
And I want to be neat.

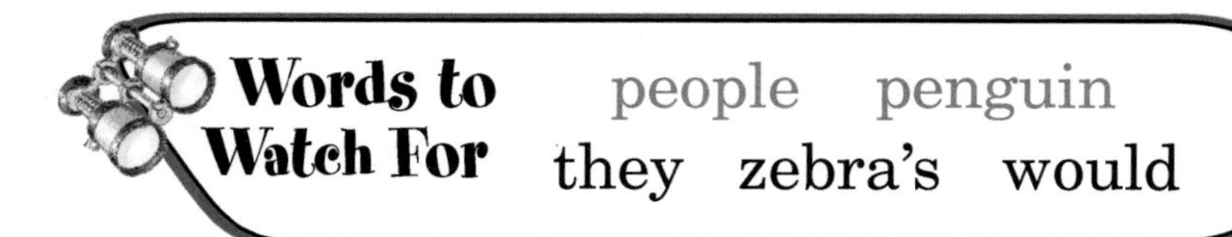

Morning at the Zoo

Cheryl Parvin

Before they open up the gates
  To let the people in,
Do you suppose the animals
  Must dress up in their skins?
And if the zebra's zipper stuck
  And penguin lost his vest,
Do you suppose the zoo would close
  Till everyone was dressed?

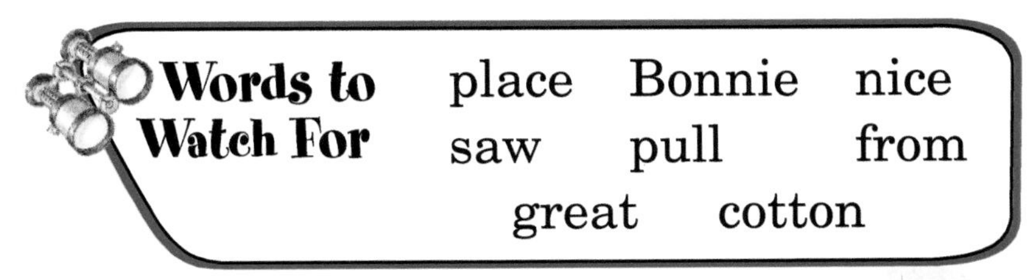

Ben Bug

Ben Bug went for a walk one day.

"I need to look for a home," he said. "I need a place for Bonnie and me. A wife needs a nice home. I want to make a nice home for Bonnie."

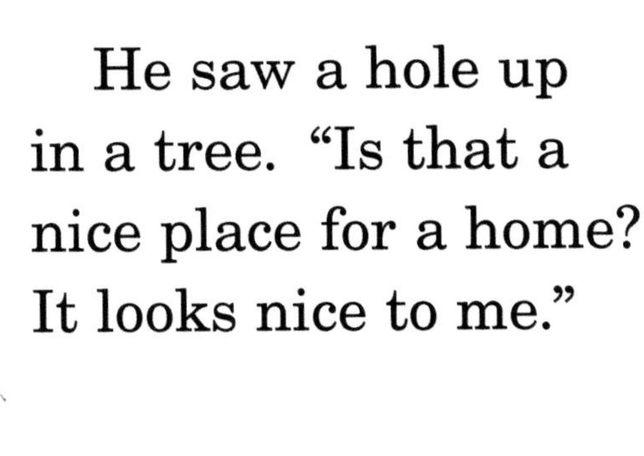

He saw a hole up in a tree. "Is that a nice place for a home? It looks nice to me."

But just then a big black bird flew by. It went into the hole.

"Oh, my, that must be his home! I can't make my home in that spot. That bird will eat Bonnie and me. Oh, no! I had better go on."

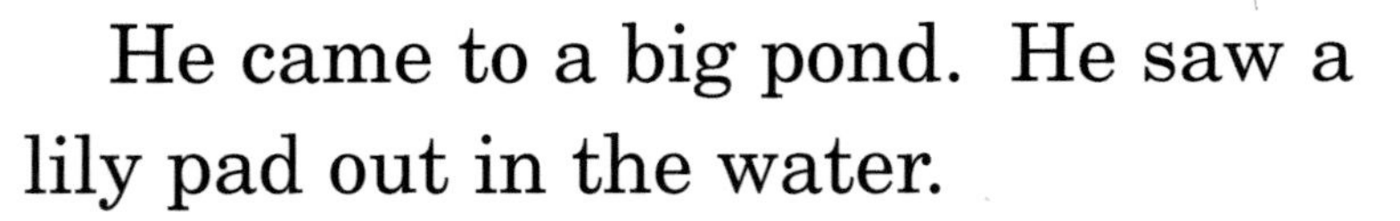

He came to a big pond. He saw a lily pad out in the water.

"How nice," he said. "A home that will float. Bonnie might like a home like a boat."

But then—oh, my! A frog hopped by. Hop, hop. Splash, splash. Up went the lily pad. Down went the lily pad in the pond.

"Oh, dear! That will not do for a home. Bonnie and I will drown. Besides, that frog likes to eat bugs. This is no place for our home. I had better go on."

Soon he came to a big patch of grass.

"What is this I see? It looks like a little jug with a small hole in it. A frog cannot get inside, and a bird cannot get in. But it is just right for me to go in."

Ben went into the jug and looked around.

"This will make a big home. I think Bonnie will like it. We will be safe in this jug.

But now I need a bed, and I need a rug. I want to make it nice for Bonnie."

Ben went out of the jug. He looked and looked. Then he saw a big rag. It was a red sock.

"Oh, this is a good rag. It is just what I need. It will make a nice rug in our home."

He had to pull and tug, but at last he had it in the jug.

"Oh, this is nice! I like it, and I think Bonnie will, too. But now I need a bed. How can I make a bed? I'll go and look for one."

He went out of his home.

He had to look and look and look. He saw a matchbox, but it was too big.

"It will not go in the hole of the jug."

Then he saw a little lid. It was the cap from a bottle of pop.

"This will be good."

"Let's see if I can get it home."

So he had to pull and tug and pull and tug. He got it up to the hole of the jug.

"Will it fit?" Pull, pull, pull.

"Look! It fits!" The cap fell into the jug.

"I'll go get Bonnie now. She must see our home."

He ran to get Bonnie. But on the way, he saw a big lid. It was the lid from a jar of jam. It had water in it, and it was close to his home.

"That will make a fine place to swim."

He climbed up a tall blade of grass.

"I can dive into the pool from this spot. Here I go!"

Splash!

Off he went to get Bonnie.

"Oh, Bonnie," he said, "You will like our home."

"Tell me about it," Bonnie said.

"It is big and nice, and we will be safe," Ben said.

Bonnie did like her home.

"I like to swim, and this pool is great," she cried. "And I like this nice red rug. But the bed—it is not good. How can we fix the bed? It is not soft."

Then she said, "Oh, Ben, I can make it soft."

She ran back to see her mom.

"Look at this, Ben," she said. "My mom had this cotton ball. It is soft."

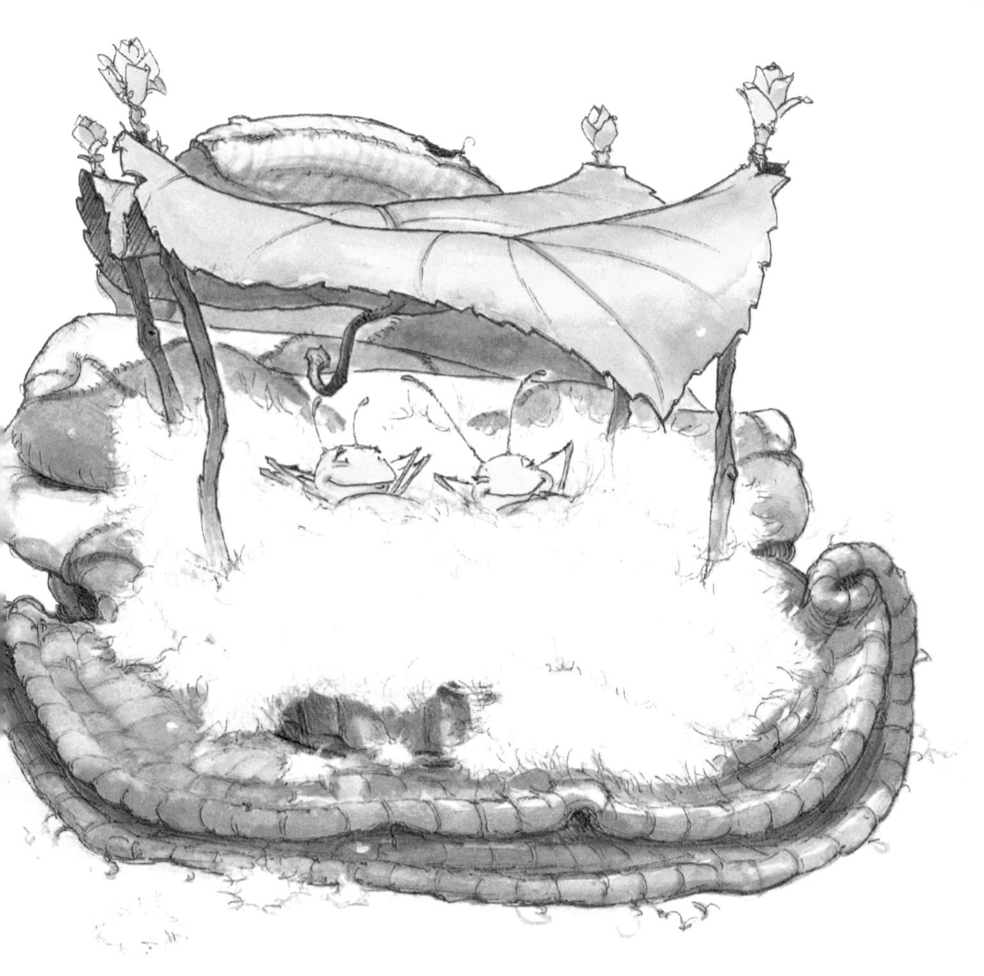

Bonnie put it in the little lid.

Bonnie was right. It made a big soft bed for two little bugs.

“Get on the bed now. See how soft it is.”

“It takes a wife to make a home nice,” said Ben.

Do You Know?

1. What things did Ben do to make the home nice?
2. What things did Bonnie do?
3. Do you think Ben is thankful for what Bonnie did?
4. Do you think Bonnie is thankful for what Ben did?

First Things First

Number these pictures in the order that they took place in the story. Put 1 in the box under the picture that shows what happened first, then 2, then 3; and put 4 under the thing that happened last.

Words to Watch For

says	turkey
head	nicest

The Turkey

The turkey is a funny bird.
His head goes wobble, wobble.
All he says is just one word,
"Gobble, gobble, gobble!"

Manners

Manners is to do and say
The nicest things in the
nicest way.

Rags

I have a dog, and his name is Rags.
He eats so much that his tummy sags.
His ears flip-flop, and his tail wig-wags.
And when he walks, he zigs and zags.

Flip-flop
Wiggle-waggle
Zig-zag

Flip-flop
Wiggle-waggle
Zig-zag

The Little Red Hen

One morning the Little Red Hen was scratching for food in the barnyard. She found a grain of wheat and called to her sleepy friends.

Little Red Hen: Who will help me plant this grain of wheat?

Her friends each opened one eye.

Dog: "Not I! I'm sleepy."

Cat: "Not I!"

Pig: "Not I!"

Duck: "Not I!"

Little Red Hen: "Then I will!"

And she planted the wheat in a corner of the barnyard. The wheat grew tall.

Soon it was ready to cut.

The Little Red Hen called to her friends. They were playing ball behind the barn.

Little Red Hen: "Who will help me cut the wheat?"

Dog: "Not I!"

Cat: "Not I! It's too hot!"

Pig: "Not I!"

Duck: "Not I!"

Little Red Hen: "Then I will!"

It was a hot job, but soon the Little Red Hen had cut all the wheat.

Little Red Hen: "Hm, the next step is to thresh the wheat."

"Threshing is hard work. I wish the dog or the pig would help me. They are stronger than I am. I will ask them."

The Little Red Hen found her friends sitting in the shade of the oak tree. They were hot after playing their ball game.

Little Red Hen: "Who will help me thresh the wheat?"

Dog: "Not I!"

Cat: "Not I!"

Pig: "Not I! I'm tired."

Duck: "Not I!"

They all sat drinking cold drinks.

Little Red Hen: "Then I will!"

It was hard work, and it took her a long time. Her friends were napping by the time she was done.

The next morning the Little Red Hen got up early. The wheat must go to the mill to be ground into flour. She looked at her sleeping friends.

Little Red Hen: "Who will help me take the wheat to the mill?"

Her friends did not even open their eyes.

Dog: "Not I!"

Cat: "Not I!"

Pig: “Not I!”

Duck: “Not I! Go away!”

They kept on sleeping.

Little Red Hen: “Then I will!”

She called all her chicks, and down the road they went to the mill.

When the Little Red Hen got back, her friends were heading for the swimming hole. Cat had a book to read.

Little Red Hen: “I’m glad I saw you! Now it’s time to make the bread. Who will help me make the flour into bread?”

Dog: “Not I! It’s too hot to cook!”

Cat: “Not I!”

Pig: “Not I!”

Duck: “Not I!”

So the Little Red Hen baked the bread and set the golden loaf on the table to cool.

Soon her friends came by on their way home from the swimming hole. They smelled the fresh bread.

Little Red Hen: "Who will help me eat this bread?"

Dog: "I will!"

Cat: "I will! It smells good."

Pig: "I will!"

Duck: "I will!"

But the Little Red Hen shook her head.

Little Red Hen: "You would not help me plant the wheat. You would not help me cut the wheat. You would not help me thresh the wheat or take it to the mill."

Little Red Hen: "You would not help me bake the bread, so you will not get to eat the bread. My chicks and I will eat it."

And they did!

Do You Know?

1. Who got to eat the bread?

*2. Do you think this was fair?

Words to Watch For		
	Hubbard	cupboard
	bare	because

Old Mother Hubbard

Old Mother Hubbard
went to the cupboard,
To get her poor dog a bone.
But when she got there,
the cupboard was bare,
And so the poor dog had none.

My Black Hen

Hickety, pickety, my black hen,
She lays eggs for gentlemen;
Sometimes nine and sometimes ten,
Hickety, pickety, my black hen.

Raining on the Farm

Laurel Hicks

The hens lay eggs in the chicken coop,
The horses munch hay in the barn,
And the children play in the house
  today,
Because it's raining on the farm.

Who and What?

Mark the ○ under the picture that answers the question.

1. What did the Little Red Hen find in the barnyard?

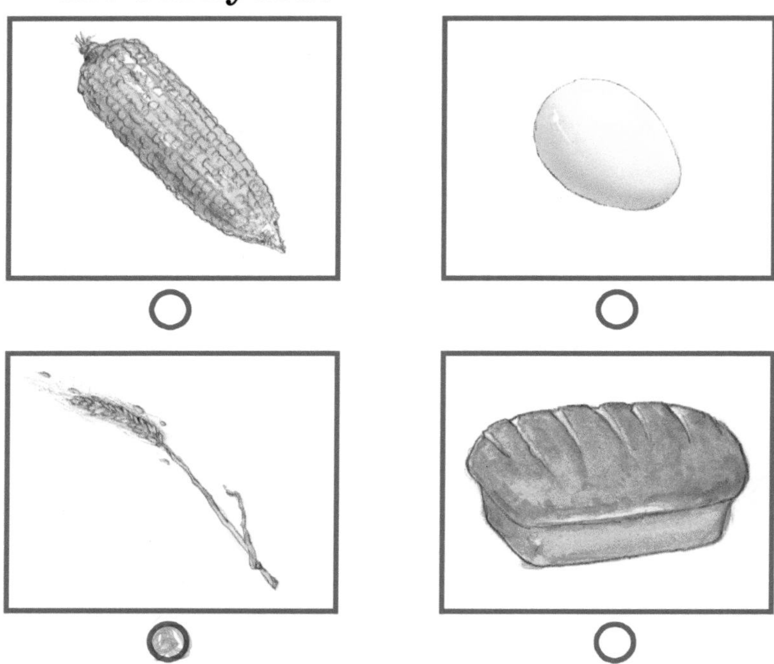

2. Who were the Little Red Hen's friends?

3. Who took the wheat to the mill?

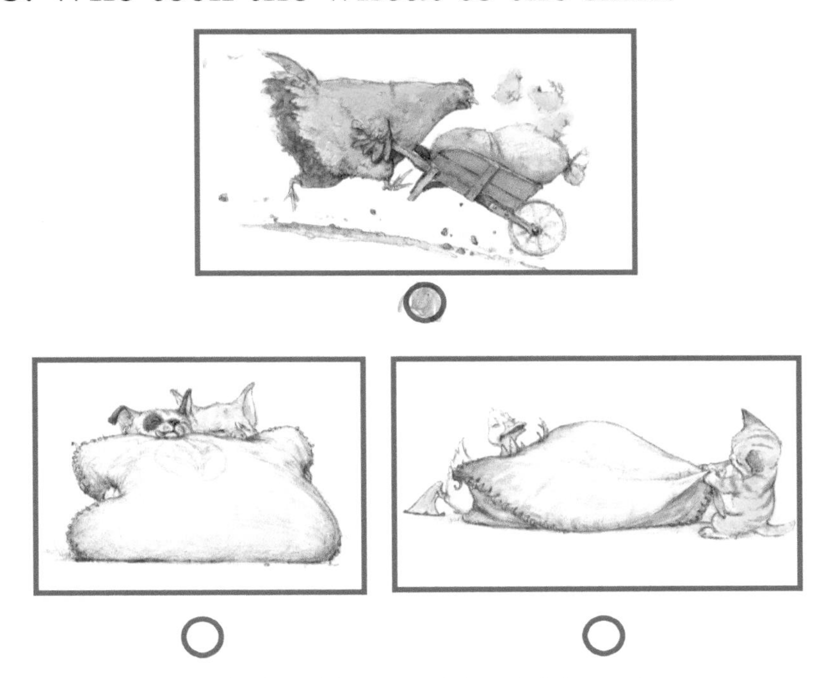

4. What did the Little Red Hen bake with the flour?

Words to Practice

Review these sight words.

build built wolf wolves

Read these words quickly.

money	voice	breath
straw	nicely	please
mother	second	put
cheap	brother	lesson
scared	chimney	lovely

The Three Little Pigs

One day a mother pig called her three little pigs and talked to them sadly.

Mother Pig: "You are growing up now. It is time for you to go out on your own. Here is some money for each of you. It will help you get started."

Mother Pig: "Be good little pigs, and watch out for the big bad wolf!"

First Little Pig: "Thank you, Mother!"

Second Little Pig: "Thank you, Mother!"

Third Little Pig: "Thank you, Mother! We will try to be good, and we will watch out for the big bad wolf."

The first two little pigs ran and skipped down the road. The third little pig was not so fast. He was looking all around for the big bad wolf. Soon the pigs came to a little town. The first little pig saw a man selling straw.

First Little Pig: "This is just what I need to build my house! Straw is cheap.

I can get all the straw I need and still have money left to get candy."

So the first little pig got lots of straw for his house. Then he got candy. But the house he built was not strong.

When the second little pig came into town, he saw a man selling sticks.

Second Little Pig: "This is just what I need to build my house! A house built of sticks will not take much money. I will be able to get a nice toy, too."

So the second little pig got a bundle of sticks to build his house. Then he got a boat at the toy store. But the house he built was not sturdy.

When the third little pig came to town, he saw a man selling bricks.

Third Little Pig: "This is just what I need to build my house. Bricks will make a strong house. It will keep me safe from the wolf."

So the third little pig got a load of bricks. It took him a long time to build his strong house.

It was not long before the wolf heard that the pigs had left home and had each built a house. He put on his best coat and hat and rushed out.

Soon he found the first little pig's house of straw. He knocked on the door and said in a high, sweet voice,

Wolf: "Little Pig, Little Pig, let me come in."

The pig peeked out a hole in his house and saw the wolf!

First Little Pig: "Not by the hair of my chinny-chin-chin."

Wolf: "Then I'll huff, and I'll puff, and I'll blow your house in!"

The wolf got a big breath. Then he huffed, and he puffed, and he blew the straw house down.

Meanwhile, the little pig ducked out the back and ran all the way to the second little pig's house.

First Little Pig: "Please let me in, dear Brother! The wolf came and blew my house down!"

The second little pig heard his brother's voice. He opened the door quickly and let him in.

It did not take the wolf long to find the house made of sticks. He put on a big smile and then knocked on the door.

Wolf: "Little Pig, Little Pig, please let me come in." He spoke in that same high, sweet voice.

But the second little pig peeked out the window and knew it was the wolf.

Second Little Pig: "Not by the hair of my chinny-chin-chin."

Wolf: "Then I'll huff, and I'll puff, and I'll blow your house in!"

The wolf got a big breath, and he huffed, and he puffed, and soon the house was just a pile of sticks on the ground. But the first and second little pigs had gotten out the back, and now they ran all the way to the third little pig's house.

They banged on the door of the brick house.

Second Little Pig: “Please let us in, dear Brother! The wolf has blown down our houses of straw and sticks. We need a strong house to hide in.”

The third little pig heard his brother’s voice and opened the door. The pigs rushed in. He saw how scared they were. He started to tell them that they had been foolish to use part of their money on candy and toys, but he knew they had learned a good lesson.

Third Little Pig: “Quick! Put the big kettle on to boil! The wolf will be here soon!”

It did not take the wolf long to find the house made of bricks. He walked round and round it.

He saw the strong walls and the thick door.

He saw the big sturdy chimney.

He knew the third little pig had worked hard on his house.

The wolf put on his best smile and fixed his hat so that his ears did not show. He spoke in his sweetest voice.

Wolf: "Little Pig, Little Pig, let me come in. This is not the big, bad wolf. I've come to see your lovely house."

But the pigs had seen the wolf out the window. They had seen the big tail showing under the coat.

Third Little Pig: "Not by the hair of my chinny-chin-chin!"

Wolf: "Then I'll huff, and I'll puff, and I'll blow your house in."

The wolf huffed, and he puffed, but the house did not come down.

He took a bigger breath, and he huffed, and he puffed, and then he puffed, and he huffed, but still the house did not fall down. The wolf lay on the ground panting, all out of breath.

Then he looked up and saw the big chimney. He had a plan. He went around to the back of the house and climbed up on the roof.

Wolf: "I'll get them yet! I'll come down the chimney."

Third Little Pig: "I hear him on the roof! I'll take the lid off the big kettle!"

The third little pig rushed to the pot. The water was boiling nicely.

Just then the wolf fell down the chimney right into the pot.

The smart little pig popped the lid on top of the kettle. His brothers cheered! That was the end of the big bad wolf!

From then on all three brothers stayed in the brick house. They watched out for wolves, and they spent money wisely.

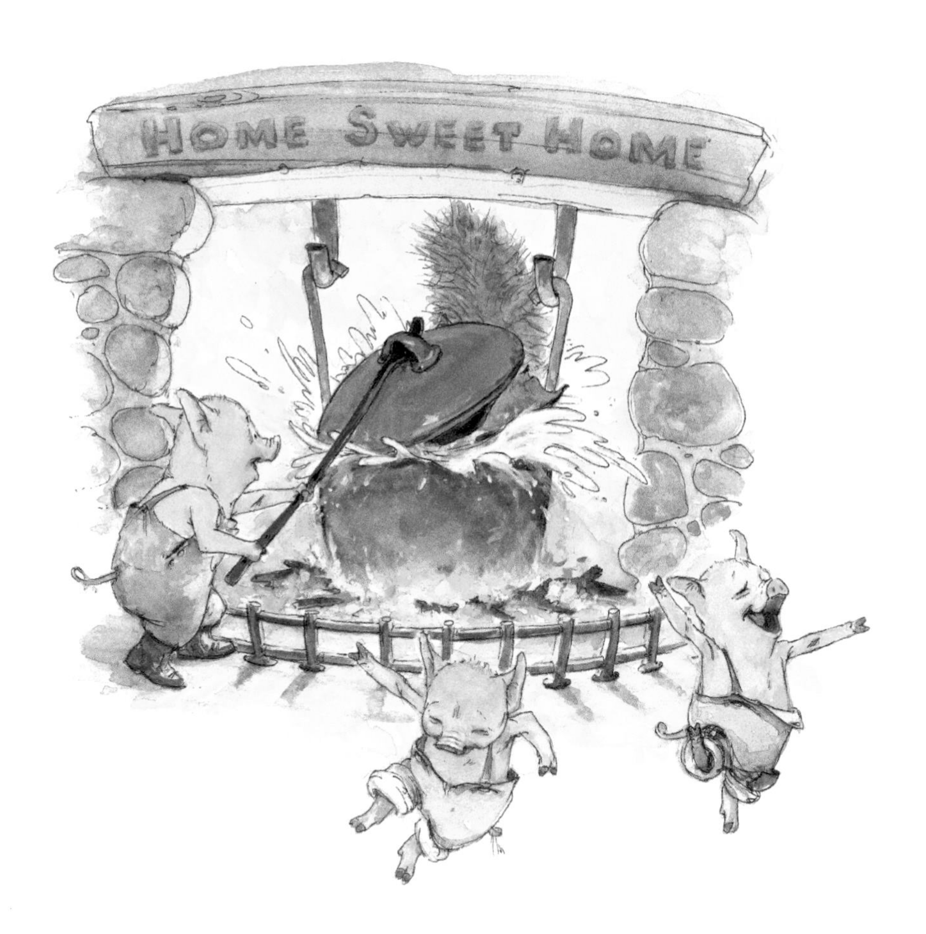

Do You Know?

1. What advice did the mother pig give her sons?

2. Was it good advice?

*3. Why should we listen to our mothers?

Which Words?

Look at the pictures below. There are two rows of words to go with each one. One word in each row will remind you of the animal in the picture. Mark the ○ under those words.

sticks straw bricks

work toy candy

sticks straw bricks

work toy candy

sticks straw bricks

work toy candy

Fuzzy Wuzzy

Fuzzy Wuzzy was a bear.
Fuzzy Wuzzy had no hair.
Then Fuzzy Wuzzy
wasn't fuzzy, was he?

Alexander Alligator

Laurel Hicks

Alexander Alligator
wears a happy grin
Starting at his earholes
and reaching to his chin.

Words to Watch For squeak caw

Bow-Wow, Says the Dog

Bow-wow, says the dog;
Mew, mew, says the cat;
Oink, oink, says the hog;
And squeak, says the rat.

To who? says the owl;
Caw, caw, says the crow;
Quack, quack, says the duck;
And moo, says the cow.

Words to Watch For lived always could

Animal Alphabet

A was an ant
Who seldom stood still,
And who made a nice house
In the side of a hill.
a
Nice little ant!
—Edward Lear

B was a bat
Who slept all the day,
And fluttered about
When the sun went away.
b
Brown little bat!
—Edward Lear

C was a camel:
You rode on his hump;
And if you fell off,
You came down such a bump!

c

What a high camel!

—Edward Lear

D was a duck
With spots on his back,
Who lived in the water,
And always said, "Quack!"

d

Dear little duck!

—Edward Lear

E was an elephant,
Stately and wise;
He had tusks and a trunk,
And two odd little eyes.
e
Oh, what funny small eyes!
—Edward Lear

F was a fox
As sly as could be.
He watched the fat mouse
From behind the oak tree.
f
Crafty old fox!
—Marion Hedquist

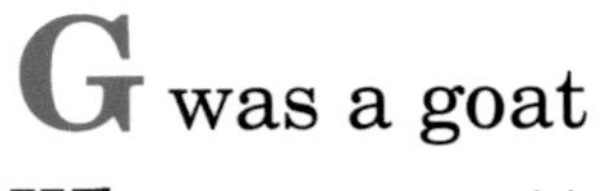

G was a goat
Who was spotted with brown;
When he did not lie still
He walked up and down.

g

Good little goat!

—Edward Lear

H was a horse
With a long flowing mane.
He ran like the wind
Across the wide plain.

h

Fast running horse!

—Marion Hedquist

I was an inchworm
Bright green on the ground.
See him hunch his back
And wiggle off to town.

i

Clever inchworm!

—Marion Hedquist

J was a jaguar
High up in the tree
With shiny green eyes
Peering down at me.

j

Sleek spotted jaguar!

—Marion Hedquist

K was a kingfisher;
Quickly he flew—
So bright and so pretty!—
Green, purple, and blue.

k

Kingfisher blue!

—Edward Lear

L was a lion,
A very large cat.
Sleeping in the sunshine,
Getting old and fat.

l

Majestic lion!

—Marion Hedquist

M was a monkey
Swinging in the tree.
Just for a joke
He might land on me!

m

Funny little monkey!

—Marion Hedquist

N was a night owl
Sleeping all day long.
He gets up at bedtime
And starts to sing his song.

n

Who-o-o-Owl-Who!

—Marion Hedquist

O was an ostrich;
He was very tall;
He stood on two legs,
And never did fall.

o

Awesome ostrich!

—Judy Hazewinkel

P was a pig
Who was not very big;
But his tail was too curly,
And that made him surly.

p

Cross little pig!

—Edward Lear

Words to Watch For

vulture
beautiful
umbrette
carry
naughty
spread
helpful

Q was a quail
With a very short tail,
And he fed upon corn
In the evening and morn.

q

Quaint little quail!

—Edward Lear

R was a rabbit,
Who had a bad habit
Of eating the flowers
In gardens and bowers.

r

Naughty, fat rabbit!

—Edward Lear

S was a seal
Who lived in the zoo.
He liked to eat fish
And play ball with you.

s

Cute little seal!

—Marion Hedquist

T was a turtle
Hiding in his shell.
If he has a name,
He will never tell.

t

Shy little turtle!

—Laurel Hicks

U was an umbrette
With a long crest.
He works hard to get
Sticks for his big nest.

u

Busy umbrette!

—Elizabeth Saylor

V was a vulture.
See his big feet?
They clutch his supper
Till he's ready to eat!

v

Hungry vulture!

—Marion Hedquist

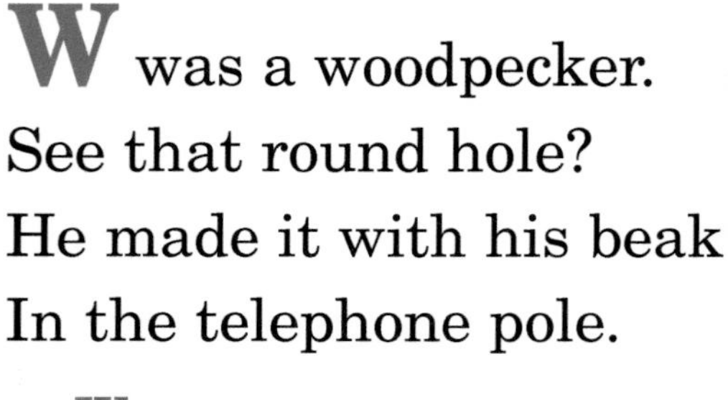

W was a woodpecker.
See that round hole?
He made it with his beak
In the telephone pole.

w

Noisy Woodpecker!

—Marion Hedquist

X was an ox.
Farmer Brown calls him "Jack."
He can carry any load
On his strong, wide back.

x

Helpful old ox!

—Marion Hedquist

Y was a yak,
From the land of Tibet.
Except his white tail,
He was all black as jet.

y

Look at the yak!

—Edward Lear

Z was a zebra,
All striped white and black;
And if he were tame
You might ride on his back.

z

Pretty striped zebra!

—Edward Lear

Do You Know?

1. Name all of the birds in the animal alphabet.

*2. Which animals would you find in a zoo?

*3. Which animals would you find on a farm?

Words to Practice

Contractions *Match each contraction with the correct two words. Draw lines to connect the ones that match.*

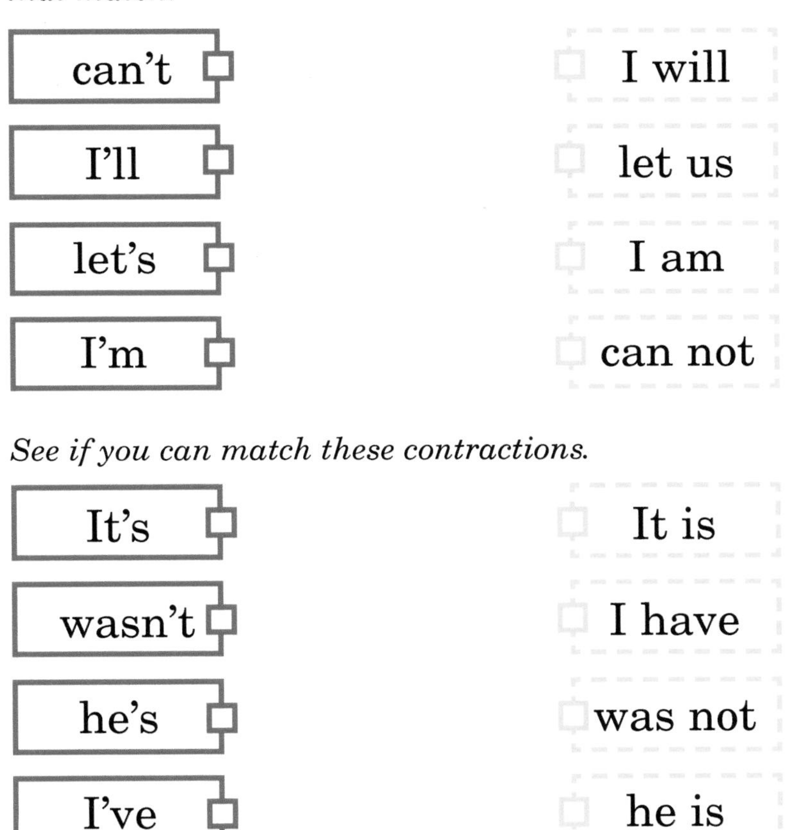

I Love to Read!

Marion Hedquist

I love to read about
Places to go and
    things to do,
Animals that live
    at the farm or the zoo.
Twins that learn on
    God to depend,
But now, it's time
    to say:

The End.